For Wally

Random House Australia, an imprint of Random Century Australia Pty Ltd
20 Alfred Street, Milsons Point, NSW 2061

Sydney Melbourne London Auckland Johannesburg and agencies throughout the world

First published in Australia in 1992

ISBN 0 09 182705 1

Cover illustration by Martin Handford
Cover design by Matthew Lilly
Printed and bound in Italy by L.E.G.O., Vicenza

MARTIN HANDFORD

RANDOM HOUSE
AUSTRALIA

HI FRIENDS!
MY NAME IS WALLY.
I'M JUST SETTING OFF ON A WORLD-WIDE HIKE.
YOU CAN COME TOO. ALL YOU HAVE TO DO IS FIND
ME, WHEREVER I GO.

I'VE GOT ALL I NEED - WALKING STICK, KETTLE,
MALLET, CUP, RUCKSACK, SLEEPING BAG,
BINOCULARS, CAMERA, SNORKEL, BELT, BAG
AND SHOVEL.

BY THE WAY, I'M NOT TRAVELLING ON MY OWN.
THAT'S MY DOG WOOF AND WENDA BEHIND
ME, AND TEN WALLY-WATCHERS. WHEREVER I
GO, WOOF AND WENDA ARE THERE SOMEWHERE
- THOUGH ALL YOU CAN EVER SEE OF WOOF IS
HIS TAIL. WATCH OUT FOR THE WALLY-WATCHERS
TOO - EACH APPEARS ONCE ON MY TRAVELS.

FIND ALL OF US, IF YOU CAN.

Wally

GREETINGS,
WALLY FOLLOWERS!
WOW, THE BEACH WAS
GREAT TODAY! I SAW
THIS GIRL STICK AN
ICE CREAM IN HER
BROTHER'S FACE, AND
THERE WAS A SAND
CASTLE WITH A REAL
KNIGHT IN ARMOUR
INSIDE! FANTASTIC!

Wally

TO:
WALLY FOLLOWERS,
HERE, THERE,
EVERYWHERE.

WHERE'S
ON THE BEACH
WALLY?

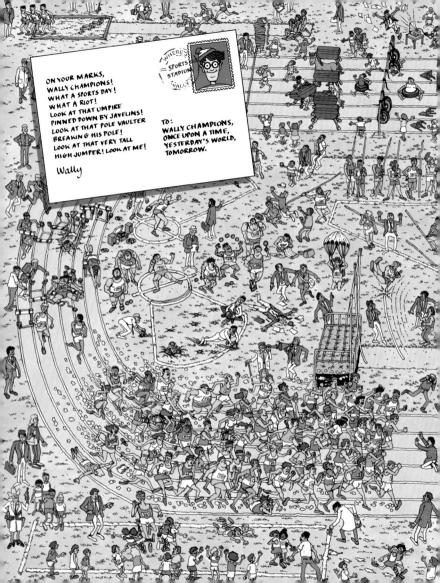

HOW-DE-DOO, WALLY SCHOLARS!
I'M CLEVER, AS YOU KNOW.
I GO TO MUSEUMS TO LEARN
THINGS. TODAY I FOUND OUT
ABOUT TICKLING THE TOES OF
A MAN IN THE STOCKS; ABOUT
KNOCKING DOWN A SUIT OF
ARMOUR; ABOUT THE
EGYPTIAN MUMMY'S BABY.
NOW THAT'S LEARNING!
HAVE YOU LEARNT TO FIND ME?

Wally

TO:
WALLY SCHOLARS,
AT SCHOOL,
IN TROUBLE,
AGAIN.

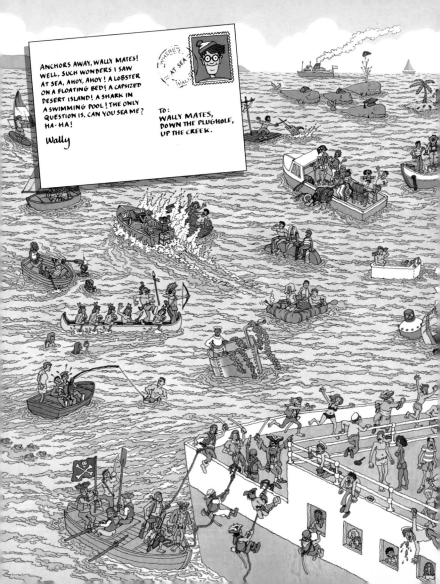

ANCHORS AWAY, WALLY MATES! WELL, SUCH WONDERS I SAW AT SEA, AHOY, AHOY! A LOBSTER ON A FLOATING BED! A CAPSIZED DESERT ISLAND! A SHARK IN A SWIMMING POOL! THE ONLY QUESTION IS, CAN YOU SEA ME? HA-HA!

Wally

TO:
WALLY MATES,
DOWN THE PLUGHOLE,
UP THE CREEK.

WATCH IT, WALLY HUNTERS!
I'M AN ANIMAL LOVER, THAT'S
FOR SURE. I LOVE THAT HIPPO
WITH ITS ALARM CLOCK; THAT
LION HAVING ITS MANE COMBED;
THE HAT-EATING GIRAFFE; THE
OWLS IN SPECTACLES. GREAT!
NOW TRACK ME DOWN, IF YOU
DARE.

Wally

TO:
WALLY HUNTERS,
NICE PLACE,
THE JUNGLE,
OUTSIDE.

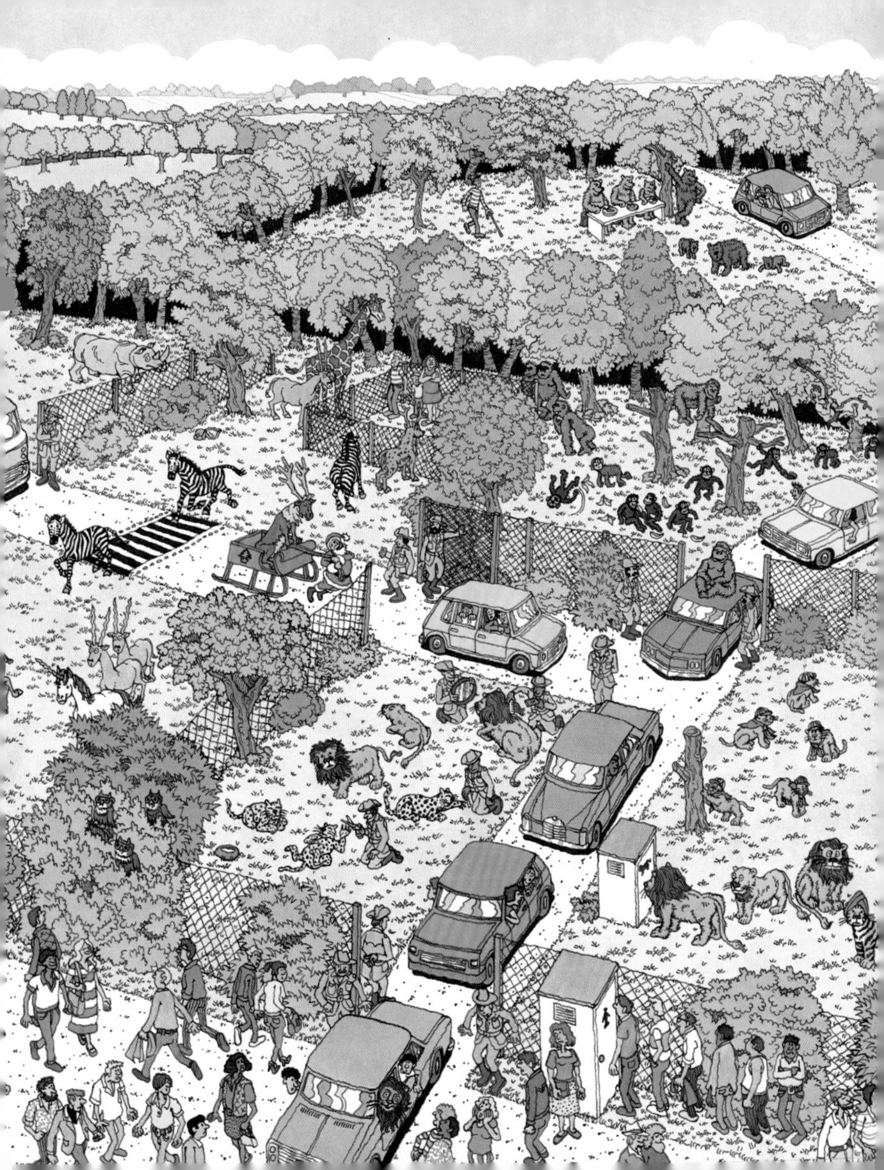

WOTCHA, WALLY WATCHERS!
SAW SOME TRULY TERRIFIC
SIGHTS TODAY - SOMEONE
BURNING TROUSERS WITH
AN IRON; A LONG THIN MAN
WITH A LONG THIN TIE;
A GLOVE ATTACKING A MAN.
PHEW! INCREDIBLE!

Wally

TO:
WALLY WATCHERS,
OVER THE MOON,
THE WILD WEST,
NOW.

THE GREAT WHERE'S WALLY? CHECK LIST
Hundreds more things for Wally watchers to watch out for!

IN TOWN
- A dog on a roof
- A man on a fountain
- A man about to trip over a dog's lead
- A car crash
- A keen barber
- People in a street, watching TV
- A puncture caused by a Roman arrow
- A tearful tune
- A boy attacked by a plant
- A waiter who isn't concentrating
- A robber who's been clobbered
- A face on a wall
- A man coming out of a man-hole
- A man feeding pigeons
- A bicycle crash

SKI SLOPES
- A man reading on a roof
- A flying skier
- A runaway skier
- A backward skier
- A portrait in snow
- An illegal fisherman
- A snowball in the neck
- Two unconscious skiers
- Two skiers hitting trees
- An Alpine horn
- A snow skier
- A flag collector
- Two very scruffy skiers
- A skier up a tree
- A water skier on snow
- A Yeti
- A skiing reindeer
- A roof jumper
- A heap of skaters

THE RAILWAY STATION
- A boy falling from a train
- A break-down on tracks
- Naughty children on a train roof
- People being knocked over by a door
- A man about to step on a ball
- Three different times at the same time
- A wheelbarrow pram
- A face on a train
- Five people reading one newspaper
- A struggling bag carrier
- A show-off with suitcases
- A man losing everything from his cases
- A squeeze on a bench
- A smoking train
- Fare dodgers
- A dog tearing a man's trousers
- A hand caught between doors
- A cattle stampede
- A man breaking a weighing machine

ON THE BEACH
- A dog biting a boy's bottom
- A man who is overdressed
- A muscular medallion man
- A popular girl
- A water skier on water
- A stripy photo
- A punctured lilo
- A donkey who likes ice-cream
- A man being squashed
- A punctured beach ball
- A human pyramid
- A human stepping-stone
- Two odd friends
- A cowboy
- A human donkey
- Age and beauty
- A boy who follows in his father's footsteps
- Two men with vests, one without
- A boy being tortured by a spider
- A show-off with sandcastles
- A gang of hat robbers
- An Arab making pyramids
- Three protruding tongues
- Two oddly fitting hats
- An odd couple
- Five sprinters
- A towel with a hole in it
- A punctured hovercraft
- A boy who's not allowed any ice-cream

CAMP SITE
- A bull in a hedge
- Bull horns
- A shark in a canal
- A bull seeing red
- A careless kick
- Tea in a lap
- A low bridge
- People knocked over by a mallet
- A man surprised undressing
- A bicycle tyre about to be punctured
- Camper's camels
- A scarecrow that doesn't work
- A wigwam
- A collapsed tent
- A smoking barbecue
- A fisherman catching old boots
- A winning penny-farthing
- Boy scouts making fire
- A roller hiker
- A man blowing up a boat
- A camper's butler
- Runners on the road
- A bull chasing children
- Scruffy campers
- Thirsty walkers

SPORTS STADIUM
- Three pairs of feet, sticking out of sand
- A cowboy starting races
- Hopeless hurdlers
- Ten children with fifteen legs
- A record thrower
- A shot-put juggler
- An ear trumpet
- A vaulting horse
- A runner with two wheels
- A parachuting vaulter
- A Scotsman with a caber
- An elephant pulling a rope
- People being knocked over by a hammer
- A gardener
- Three frogmen
- A nude runner
- A bed
- A bandaged boy
- A runner with four legs
- A sunken jumper
- A man with an odd pair of legs
- A man chasing a dog, chasing a cat
- A boy squirting water